The Animal Garden

The Animal Garden

A story by

Ogden Nash

drawings by

Hilary Knight

Published by M. Evans & Company, Inc., New York and distributed in
association with J. B. Lippincott Company, Philadelphia and New York

The walls of verse that
separate the pictures
were built with love for
Nell, Francie,
Nicky, Biddy,
and Nenna.   O.N.

                The Pecoras
                H.K.

Roy was nine and Roy loved animals,
Joy was eight and Joy loved animals,
Roy and Joy, they dreamed of animals,
Animals all night through.

Mother got cross when they begged for animals,
Daddy got cross when they begged for animals,
Both agreed there was one place for animals;
That was in the zoo.

Roy loved his mother and his father dearly,
Joy loved her mother and her father dearly,
Both loved their parents dearlier than anything—
Except, perhaps, a pet.
BUT—
Mother had a dreadful allergy to animals,
Daddy had a dreadful allergy to animals,
If anybody even mentioned animals
They got all upset.

Mother said cats brought on her asthma,
Daddy said dogs brought on *his* asthma;
If Roy said "Puppy" or Joy said "Kitten,"
Both began to wheeze.

Ducks meant sniffles and chicks meant chicken pox,
Goldfish scared them, so did hamsters,
Thoughts of parrots or canaries left them
Wobbly in the knees.

Once a swallow fell down the chimney,
Twittering, fluttering round the parlor.
Roy and Joy let it out the window;
Mother retired to bed.

Once a cricket chirped on the hearthstone;
The children found it, let it out the window.
Daddy slumped like a lump in his armchair,
Ice pack on his head.

Who was watching but Abidan Allseed,
Shriveled up, shrunken up Abidan Allseed,
Tiny and gray like an old, old dandelion,
Under the garden gate.
"This won't do," said Abidan Allseed,
Gentle old, clever old Abidan Allseed,
Allseed, Johnny Appleseed's grandpa,
Great-
Great-
Great-
Great-GREAT.
Said Abidan, "Just wait."

What can I tell you of Abidan?
Well, he wasn't a regular mortal man,
Yet he wasn't a goblin or gnome or elf,
Old Abidan, he was just himself.
He had lived in Eden, I believe,
A distant cousin of Adam and Eve,
And related, on his mother's side,
To some things from which he used to hide.
He roamed the world from Siam to Sweden
With a bulging sack he had filled in Eden
With bits of creation most confusing
That the Lord hadn't got around to using,
Which he parceled out, now there, now here,
Maybe once in a thousand year,
And no matter what humdrum he was amid,
Wonders that couldn't happen, did.
What were the wonders?
Just you wait,
Like Abidan under the garden gate.

Abidan waited, but just as soon
As a rumpled cloud had covered the moon
He stretched himself, and after a yawn,
Like a chipmunk he scurried across the lawn
And, silently as a shadow puppet
Found the tree he wanted and scurried up it,
Swung to the roof and softly crept
To the children's window while they slept.
He gave a whistle and then a second,
The children awoke and he smiled and beckoned.

Dear little Abidan,
Queer little Abidan!
Whispering, "Don't disappear, little Abidan,"
Roy and his sister in wonderment found
They were out of their beds and down on the ground.
Their shadows were one with Abidan's shadow.
They stole around the house to the meadow,
The sad little meadow where nothing grew
But witch grass, and a thistle or two.
The children of course had been taught the dangers
Of walks or talks with genial strangers,
But they followed funny old Abidan
As Hamelin children the piper man.
He wasn't mortal, he wasn't fairy,
But a mixture of magic and ordinary.
Ancient was Abidan,
Calm was Abidan.
Wise as the Twenty-third Psalm was Abidan.

Like a brave old book with a coat of dust,
Like a sword still true under years of rust,
Like farm-baked bread with an honest crust,
There was something about him you had to trust.
"It is now," said he, "my pleasant task
To answer your questions before you ask.
Towards this particular moment, my dears,
I've journeyed as many miles as years.
For these are specially special seeds
For specially *specially* special needs.
Here's a trowel and here's a hoe,
And here's my blessing to make them grow.
You'll find that for some marvelous reason
They'll flourish in any weather or season,
And when they blossom as advertised
I think you'l! be pleased, and perhaps surprised."

With that he emptied his sack on the ground
And the moonlight showed a mishmash mound
Of shriveled bulbs and withered slips
And moldy seeds and pods and pips.
"They've been waiting for you," said Abidan
"Since the very day the world began.
 Just tuck them in and cover them over
 And wait for your crop, it won't be clover.
 'Twas I taught patience to poor old Job,
 But I'm weary of wandering round the globe.
 I'm sorely in need of a short vacation
 Before I resume my peregrination,
 So I'm off, by the hair of my chinny-chin-chinny,
 To the Cloud-Cuckoo Land of Whipperginny."
 Then he crumbled to powder and blew away, sir,
 Like chalk-dust when you bang the eraser.

Instead of asking useless questions
They followed Abidan's suggestions.
They worked like gardeners, worked like farmers,
Got mud on the knees of their clean pajamas,
And by the end of that hour enchanted
There wasn't a seedlet left unplanted.

Then they each took a bath to remove the grime
And slept right through their breakfast time.

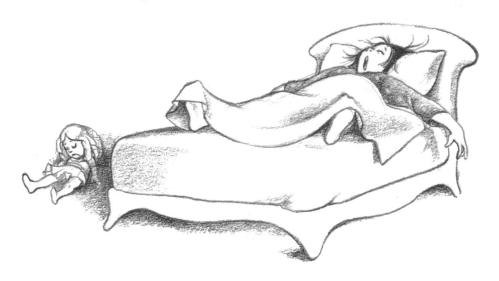

"Ahoy!" cried Roy,
"I wonder, Joy,
  How does our garden grow?
  What is the yield
  Of the midnight field
  That we planted all a-row?"
  Then they stared in horror at one another
  At a shout from Daddy, a shriek from Mother.

The air was filled with a clamor appalling
Of howling, yowling and caterwauling,
Mewing, mooing,
Chirping, cooing,
Cackling, cock-a-doodle-doing,
Snorting, squawking, squealing, yapping,
Huffling, snuffling, grunting, flapping,
Whinnying, trumpeting, bellowing, bleating,
Every kind of animal greeting.
"I think we'd better go see," said Roy.
"I think so too," said Joy.

Now, Roy and Joy had often dozed
Through their weekly class in botany;
I'm afraid they were wrongly inclined to think
That botany meant monotony.

But the sight botanic they now beheld
Would have wakened a sleeping possum,
For every plant had an animal name
And a living animal blossom.

The Lamb's-toes pattered like summer rain,
Happy without a shepherd,
Playing a game of peek-a-baa
With the Leopard Lily leopard.

The Horsemint horse was hefty enough
To pull a circus wagon,
And he sniffed the smoke from the Dragon's-mouth
Of a small and friendly dragon.

The Moosewood stamped and the Buckthorn bucked
Like spirited unicorns,
The Buffalo Currant pawed the ground
And the Cowslip tossed its horns.

The Crowberries cawed and the Dove Tree cooed,
The Bee Balm started to hum,
And all the Gooseberries cackled and honked,
But the Oyster Plant was mum.

The Goatsbeards wagged as they chewed their lips
While solving the Monkey Puzzle,
But the Wolfsbane simply sat and watched
With a gentle smile on his muzzle.

The Kangaroo Vine leaped high in joy
As Marlborough did at Blenheim,
And the jaws of the Rattlesnake Fern were filled
With honey instead of venom.

As far as the Rabbit-ears could hear
Or the Pheasant's-eye could see,
The animals voiced their best regards
From flower and vine and tree.

They had all been together
Since the days of Genesis,
All of them amicable,
None of them menaces.

Oh, pity now poor Roy and Joy
Who knelt before their parents
To tell the tale of Abidan
And beg their kind forbearance.

But from the sky there came a cry,
"Good gracious, I forgot
To say there's not an allergy
In all the blessed lot!"

And Mother with a startled look
Exclaimed, "I haven't sneezed!"
And Daddy added, "Nor have I!"
So both of them were pleased.

Then give three cheers, or better yet, four
For Abidan Allseed and his lore of yore.
The children found their rapturous glee by Daddy's
    glee was matched;
He likes to scratch the Elephant's-ear with the
    elephant attached,
And Mother pets the Lion's-tail a dozen times a day,
She even admires the Skunk Spruce, from a giant
    step away.
Joy loves her Willow-pussy, and Roy his
    Dogwood pup,
And they'll all dance around the clock when the
    Cuckooflower comes up.

What a lucky family, didn't care a sou
Were they in a garden or were they in a zoo.
Singing with the Larkspur, round and round
    they whirled
In the one and only Animal-Garden-in-the-World.

But . . .

. . . remember, it was only the-one-and-only *then*.
Who knows when Abidan will come around again?
Roaming through the seasons hot or cold or wet,
Looking for a boy or girl who's longing for a pet,
Over country acres, over city blocks,
With seeds for a garden or perhaps a window box.
So if you're very special, if you're very good,
If you learn to tend a pet exactly as you should,
Perhaps you'll hear a whistle after prayers are said,
Or a tapping on the pane after you're in bed.
It could be the wind, it could be Superman,
But if you are lucky, it might be Abidan!